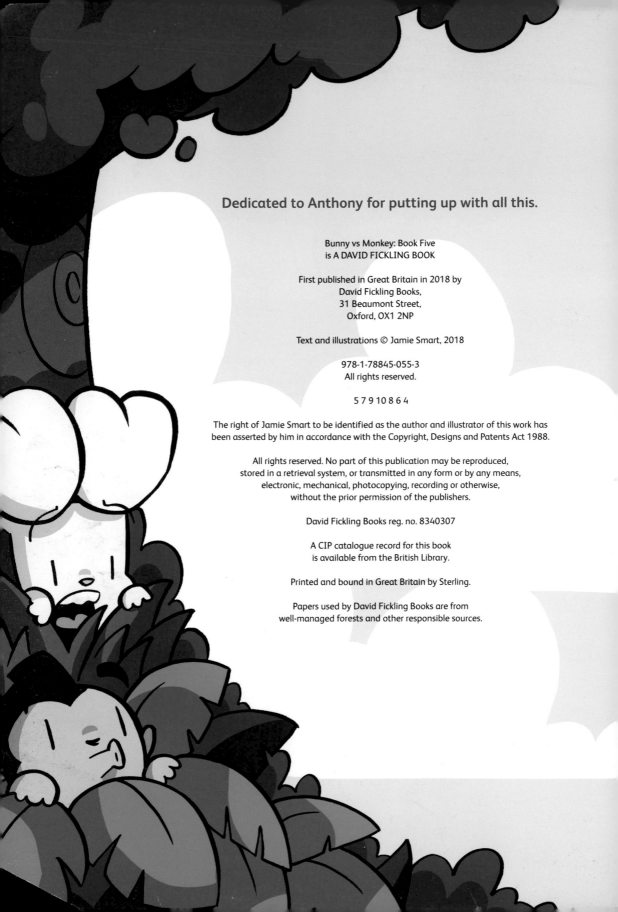

Dedicated to Anthony for putting up with all this.

Bunny vs Monkey: Book Five
is A DAVID FICKLING BOOK

First published in Great Britain in 2018 by
David Fickling Books,
31 Beaumont Street,
Oxford, OX1 2NP

Text and illustrations © Jamie Smart, 2018

978-1-78845-055-3
All rights reserved.

5 7 9 10 8 6 4

The right of Jamie Smart to be identified as the author and illustrator of this work has
been asserted by him in accordance with the Copyright, Designs and Patents Act 1988.

All rights reserved. No part of this publication may be reproduced,
stored in a retrieval system, or transmitted in any form or by any means,
electronic, mechanical, photocopying, recording or otherwise,
without the prior permission of the publishers.

David Fickling Books reg. no. 8340307

A CIP catalogue record for this book
is available from the British Library.

Printed and bound in Great Britain by Sterling.

Papers used by David Fickling Books are from
well-managed forests and other responsible sources.

CONT-ENTS!

NEXT TIME: "TOBOG-GONE!"

"METAL STEVE 2"

YOU TWO! WHAT ARE YOU DOING?

I'M BEING A **REINDEER!**

AND I'M BEING LAZY!

WELL, STOP IT. I NEED YOUR HELP. DO EITHER OF YOU KNOW HOW I TURN THIS ROBOT THING ON?

I'VE **POKED** HIM AND **JABBED** HIM AND **ROLLED HIM DOWN A HILL,** BUT **NOTHING!** HE **REFUSES** TO TURN ON!

WHAP!

HOW AM I SUPPOSED TO USE HIM TO TAKE OVER THE WOODS IF HE **WILL NOT TURN ON?!**

SORRY, MONKEY, BUT WE'RE NOT VERY CLEVER AT THINGS.

BUNNY SAYS WE'RE 'GRADUAL'!

RRGH!! THIS IS **INTOLERABLE! SKUNKY** KNOWS HOW TO TURN HIM ON, BUT **HE'S** DESERTED ME. **BUNNY** COULD WORK IT OUT, BUT **HE'D** JUST TELL ME OFF! LE FOX WON'T TALK TO ANYONE, ACTION BEAVER IS EATING WORMS, SO ALL I HAVE LEFT IS **YOU TWO.** AND YOU'RE **BOTH IDIOTS!**

I CAN BE YOUR ROBOT.

YOU...

WAIT, WHAT?

BZZ! I AM A ROBOT!

BZZ!

BZZ!

HEE HEE!

SIGH. IT MIGHT JUST HAVE TO DO.

NEXT TIME: "DESTRUCTO!"

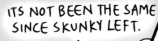

NEXT TIME: "THE MESSAGE"

"SKUNKY"

FOOLISH WOODLAND CREATURES! THE ALL-POWERFUL **SKUNKY**, HAS RETURNED TO GIVE YOU **DIRE WARNING!**

GASP! **SKUNKY!**

DID YOU TAKE A HEAD-GROWING PILL OR SOMETHING?

UMM...YES? WHY NOT. LET'S GO WITH THAT.

WE BOW TO YOU, OH, BIG FAT-HEAD SKUNKY!

I COULD GET USED TO THIS.

LESS OF THE 'FAT-HEAD' THOUGH.

I'LL GO AND GET BUNNY! HE'LL BE **AMAZED!**

WHAT? NO! DON'T GET BUNNY! HE'LL WORK OUT HOW I'M DOING THIS!

WELL, IT'S OBVIOUSLY SOME KIND OF **HOLOGRAM!**

AWWW.

I **TOLD** YOU HE'D WORK IT OUT.

NO MATTER! I GAVE YOU ALL A CHANCE TO LEAVE THESE WOODS BUT YOU HAVEN'T. SO NOW, YOU WILL ALL **SUFFER MY WRATH!**

HANG ON.

IF THIS IS A HOLOGRAM, IS THE **ACTUAL** SKUNKY FILMING THIS FROM INSIDE THAT BIG TEMPLE WE FOUND OVER THE HILL?

YES. I MEAN, NO!

I KNEW IT. I KNEW THAT'S WHERE YOU'VE BEEN HIDING!

"ALAN"

I AM **A.L.A.N.**, THE ARMOURED LOCATING ARMADILLO NETWORK. A MECHANISED **BOUNTY HUNTER** WHO KNOWS **NO FEAR!**

I'M PIG, AND I'M EATING ICE CREAM.

CHOOM!

DON'T WORRY, PIG! I CAUGHT HIM IN A **PILLOWCASE!**

SHOOM!

WOOM!

ERK!

YOUR CHILDISH DEFENCES WON'T STOP ME!

ACTIVATE SOFT LANDING!

VTT!

THRPPPP!

OH, FANCY.

DON'T WORRY ABOUT ME.

I WILL NOT.

20

WEENIE! LEAD HIM INTO THE TRAP WE BUILT FOR MONKEY!

OH... OH... OKAY!

THIS WAY, MISTER ALAN! FOLLOW ME!

FREE BANANAS

FLUMP!

FREE BANANAS

COME ON IN! IT'S LOVELY!

UHH, NO. I DON'T THINK I WILL.

HAR HAR!

THEY'RE **IDIOTS**, ALAN. I'LL PROBABLY DESTROY THEM ONE DAY, BUT YOU CAN GO AHEAD AND DO IT NOW IF YOU LIKE.

ALAN, DID SKUNKY SEND YOU? ARE YOU HIS NEW INVENTION?

I COME FROM THE FACILITY. I DO NOT KNOW THIS 'SKUNKY'.

I WAS A NORMAL ARMADILLO UNTIL THEY WEAPONISED ME INTO THE **ULTIMATE SOLDIER**. BUT I ESCAPED, AND NOW I ROAM THE WOODS SEARCHING FOR MY NEXT PREY.

SOUNDS LIKE JUST WHAT I NEED! WORK FOR ME!

NO, ALAN! FIGHT ON OUR SIDE!

YOU ARE A BRAVE BUNNY TO EVEN **ATTEMPT** TO DEFEAT ME.

BUT I ONLY WORK FOR PAYMENT.

I HAVE BANANAS.

IT IS NOT ENOUGH. PERHAPS ONE DAY WE WILL BE ALLIES.

PERHAPS ONE DAY, ENEMIES.

I GOT MORE ICE CREAM...

OOF!

BUMP!

CALL HIM OFF!

SORRY AL... THAT'S OUR **P.I.G. PLENTIFUL ICE CREAM** UMM... EATER.

THAT SPELLS PIE.

SHH.

NEXT TIME: "GET FIT!"

OOF! WEENIE, THOSE WERE THE MOST DELICIOUS FLOPPLEBERRY PIES YOU'VE EVER BAKED! I AM SO STUFFED!

IT FEELS LIKE I HAVE FOOD COMING OUT OF MY EYES!!

I CAN'T GET UP TO WEE!

!!!

HARHAR! LOOK AT YOU LOT! YOU'RE ALL OUT OF SHAPE AND SWEATY!

IN FACT, YOU'LL BE COMPLETELY UNABLE TO STOP MY DEVIOUS SCHEMES!

WAIT THERE! DON'T MOVE! I'M GOING TO FIND A DEVIOUS SCHEME TO DO!

GASP! HE'S RIGHT! WE CAN'T PROTECT THE WOODS LIKE THIS!

WE NEED TO GET FIT! AND TO DO THAT, WE'LL NEED SOMEONE TO TRAIN US WITH NO MERCY!

HELLO? LE FOX? WE NEED YOUR HELP!

MOI? PAH, WHY WOULD YOU NEED ME? I WORK ALONE.

WE'VE ALL LET OURSELVES GET UNFIT!

THE STATE WE'RE IN, MONKEY COULD JUST ROLL US DOWN A HILL!

HMM, HE WOULD ENJOY THAT. AND I REFUSE TO LET MONKEY HAVE ANY FUN!

VERY WELL, I WILL HELP. BUT MY EXERCISE REGIME WILL BE RUTHLESS!

23

NEXT TIME: "THE WRONG EGGS!"

NEXT TIME: "THE TEMPLE!"

"THE TEMPLE"

THERE IT IS! THE TEMPLE WHERE SKUNKY NOW LIVES...

...HIS NEW, SUPER-SECRET LABORATORY!

AND IF PIG HAD REMEMBERED TO BRING THE BINOCULARS, I WOULDN'T BE LOOKING AT IT THROUGH TWO **TOILET ROLLS.**

I THOUGHT THOSE **WERE BINOCCLERS.**

NO MATTER! WE CAME HERE TO SNEAK INSIDE, TO INFILTRATE SKUNKY'S INGENIOUS SECURITY SYSTEM, AND FIND OUT WHAT'S GOING ON IN THERE.

YAYYY! CHARGE!! CHARRRGE!

NO! QUIETLY!

SHH! SHH!

KICK IT! HEE HEE HEE! RFF!

RRF! WE'RE KICKING IT!

RRF!

KICK! KICK!

BEWOO! BEW BEWOOO! B

WE SET OFF AN ALARM!

WE'RE SORRY! WE DIDN'T MEAN TO KICK IT!

BEWOOO!

IT'S JUST ACTION BEAVER MAKING NOISES. WE'RE SAFE FOR NOW.

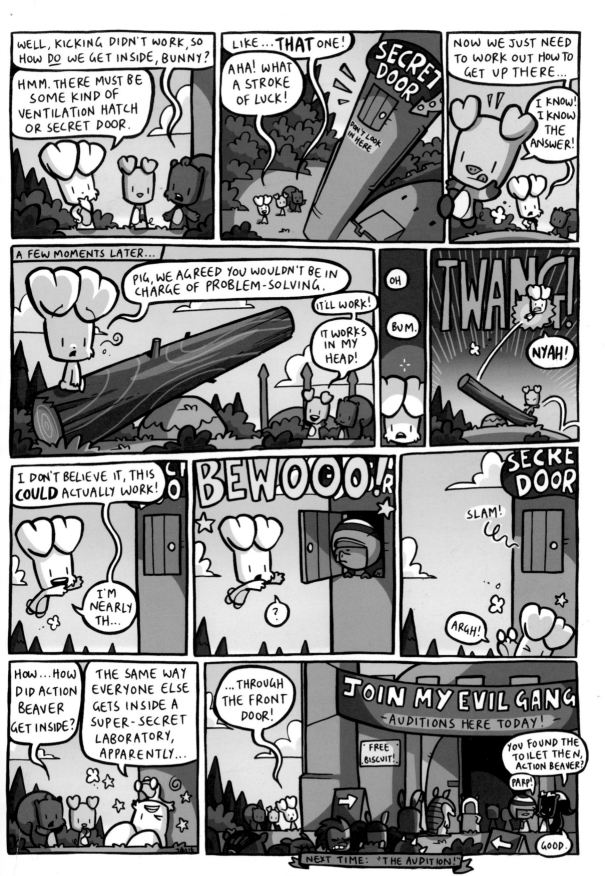

RRGH!! EVERY EVIL GENIUS NEEDS AN EVIL GANG TO CARRY OUT HIS EVIL WHIMS.

BUT GETTING A GANG TOGETHER IS HARDER THAN IT LOOKS!

AHEM!

I'M MONK... MICKEY... MIKEY! I'M MIKEY! AND I'M A SUPER TOUGH GUY! GRRR!

SIGHHH. MONKEY, THAT'S YOU.

WHO IS THIS 'MONKEY'? I'M MIKEY! I'LL FIGHT EVERYONE!

MONKEY, YOU'RE HOLDING UP THE AUDITION.

BUT HOW DID YOU KNOW IT WAS MEEEE? I'M WEARING THIS AMAZING DISGUISE!

OH, Y'KNOW.

JUST A HUNCH.

PLEEEEASE LET ME JOIN YOUR EVIL GANG, SKUNKY! OH PLEASE OH PLEASE OH PLEASE! I'M SO EVIL!

NO, YOU'RE AN IDIOT. YOU ALWAYS RUIN EVERYTHING!

I DON'T! I DON'T!

TO BE IN MY GANG, YOU NEED TO BE A REAL VILLAIN. STRONG, MEAN, AND COOL.

LIKE, UM...

LIKE...

...THAT GUY.

WHAT? THAT'S JUST PIG IN A CYCLE HELMET!

SAFETY FIRST!

NONSENSE! LOOK AT THIS GUY, HE'S CLEARLY BRUTAL!

MY NAME IS, UM... PIGULUS! CAN I BE IN YOUR CLUB PLEASE?

YEAH! YOU CAN!

WHAT?

RIGHT, GO HOME EVERYONE. I HAVE MY GANG NOW! BYE!

WHAT?

SKUNKY, YOU CAN'T SHUT ME OUT HERE WITH THESE LOSERS!

SLAM!

OH, HANG ON, YOU ALL HEARD THAT, DIDN'T YOU?

BZZ! POW! EEK! BASH! OW!

COME, NEW COHORT! OUR LEAGUE OF DOOM HAS MUCH TO DO!

BUNNY DIDN'T SEND ME!

I DIDN'T SAY HE DID.

JAMIE

NEXT TIME: "PIGULUS!"

33

APRIL

"PIG-ULUS!"

WELCOME, FELLOW EVIL-DOERS, TO YOUR NEW HOME - MY NOT-SO-SECRET SECRET H.Q., FROM WHERE WE WILL PLAN OUR DEVIOUS SCHEMES, AND SCHEME OUR DEVIOUS PLANS.

WELCOME, TO THE **LEAGUE** of **DOOM!**

— IN "PIGULUS!"

I DON'T THINK I SHOULD BE HERE.

WHAT'S THAT, PIGULUS? I COULDN'T HEAR YOU FROM THIS END OF OUR RIDICULOUSLY LONG TABLE.

I SAID, UMM... I NEED A WEE.

OH, OF COURSE! THROUGH THE DOOR, TURN LEFT, PAST THE **MEGA-RAY** DOWN THE STAIRS, BY THE **DESTRUCTO-TRON**, THIRD DOOR ON YOUR RIGHT.

THANK YOU! GIBBER!

I CAN'T KEEP PRETENDING LIKE THIS. I'M NOT EVIL! I'M A PIG!

OH, WHY DID BUNNY EVER TALK ME INTO THIS?

A LITTLE WHILE EARLIER...

ONE OF US NEEDS TO SNEAK INTO SKUNKY'S LAIR, IN A DISGUISE, TO FIND OUT HIS SECRETS!

I'LL DO IT!

DO WHAT?

NOW I'M STUCK IN AN **EVIL LAIR** AND I DON'T KNOW WHAT TO DO AND I STILL **REALLY NEED A WEE!!**

MAYBE THE TOILET IS THROUGH THIS DOOR MARKED 'WORLD-DESTROYING ARTILLERY.'

CREAK!

"THE EVIL MONKEY!"

AHA-HA-HAA! I, THE EVIL MONKEY, THE MOST CRUEL AND EVIL MONKEY IN THE ENTIRE UNIVERSE, HAVE FINALLY ARRIVED ON A DISTANT PLANET!

AND NOW I SHALL TAKE IT OVER AND RULE IT AS I SEE FIT...

...CRUELLY AND EVILLY!

WHAT?

WHO ARE YOU? WHAT'S GOING ON?

DIDN'T YOU HEAR WHAT I JUST SAID? I AM THE EVIL MONKEY!

LIKE YOU, BUT EVIL.

BUT I'M ALREADY EVIL. THERE CAN'T BE ANOTHER ME!

NOPE! I AM THE EVILLEST!

PROPER EVIL.

WHERE DID ANOTHER MONKEY COME FROM?

I DON'T KNOW, BUT HE LOOKS MORE EVIL.

HE DOES NOT!

YOU'D BETTER STAY OUT OF MY WAY, LESS-EVIL MONKEY! I'M GOING TO BE VERY BUSY, BEING EVIL!

NOT AS BUSY AS ME! I'M THE ONLY EVIL MONKEY ROUND HERE!

MEANWHILE, AT THE BRITISH SPACE PROGRAMME...

WELL, THAT'S ANOTHER MONKEY WE'VE FIRED INTO SPACE AND LOST IN THE WOODS!

MONKEY STATUS

CRASHED

HMM. THINK WE SHOULD HAVE FOUND THE FIRST ONE FIRST?

MEH.

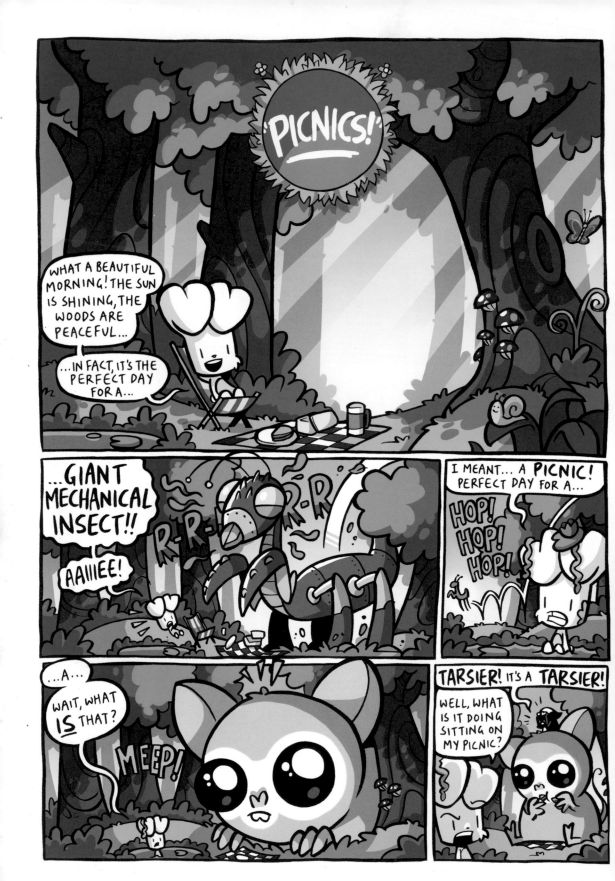

I MUST PROTECT BUNNY AND HIS FRIENDS! I HAVE WRONGED THEM IN ZE PAST.

WELL, MAYBE I CAN HELP, EH? I DID USED TO BE QUITE THE **SUPERSPY** BACK IN MY DAY.

WHY, I SINGLE-HANDEDLY BROUGHT DOWN THE NAZIS WHILE DRESSED AS A PANDA!

I CAN'T REMEMBER WHY I WAS DRESSED LIKE THAT, TO BE HONEST.

THERE'S NO NEED TO MAKE UP STORIES JUST TO IMPRESS **ME**, UNCLE.

AW, OKAY.

I NEED TO FIND A WAY TO STOP **SKUNKY**. HE'S ALREADY RUN ME OVER ONCE TODAY.

WELL, YOU KNOW WHAT WE FOXES SAY?

TWO FOXES ARE ONE MORE FOX THAN ONE FOX.

UMM..

WE CAN USE THE SECRET NETWORK OF TUNNELS WE DUG TOGETHER BACK WHEN YOU WERE A CUB.

THE PERFECT SHORTCUT.

AND WE'RE HERE.

HALT, SO-CALLED 'SKUNKY'.

GASPPP!

SCREEECH!

TWO FOXES, ONE A BIT POSH?

AH, YOU'RE DRIVING A MODIFIED **MARK 6** ARMOURED VEHICLE, EH? I KNOW IT WELL, USED TO DRIVE ONE IN LE MANS.

IF YOUR PLAN IS TO **BORE** US TO DEATH, IT WON'T WORK! WE CAN STILL GET TO BUNNY'S HOUSE BY AIR!

BOOP!

EJECTOR SEATS

EJECT!

DOOF! DOOF! DOOF!

WONDERFUL DRIVE, THE MARK 6. FAMOUS FOR ITS **EJECTOR SEATS**, WE JUST NEEDED THEM TO PARK UNDER A **TREE**.

YOU... YOU REALLY WERE A SUPERSPY?

OF COURSE, DEAR BOY. SOME OF US DON'T **NEED** TO MAKE UP OUR STORIES.

EH?

BRUMM!!

NEXT TIME - "BAD NEIGHBOUR!"

41

MAY

"BAD NEIGHBOUR!"

MORNING, NEIGHBOUR!

?

I'M BERT WARTHOG, I JUST MOVED IN NEXT DOOR. I...I DIDN'T REALISE I HAD A NEXT DOOR.

YES, MY ESTATE AGENT, MISTER MONKEY, HAD THE HOUSE BUILT OVERNIGHT!

AH, YOU'VE BOTH MET!

I SHOULD HAVE KNOWN!

WELL, I THOUGHT, IF I'M GOING TO BE EVIL I MAY AS WELL MAKE SOME MONEY AT IT.

SO NOW I'M IN THE PROPERTY MARKET!

YOU BUILT A HOUSE HERE JUST TO ANNOY ME?

YES! WELL, YOU SAY 'HOUSE', IT'S MADE OUT OF CARDBOARD AND CHEWING GUM, BUT DON'T TELL OUR NEW TENANT THAT.

BUT I LIKE MY PRIVACY.

WINK!

I'LL LEAVE YOU TWO TO GET ALONG, THEN. HAR HAR!

OH, ARE THOSE FOR ME?

CHOMP!

LOVELY.

FOUND THE PROBLEM— A **GLAZED DOUGHNUT** STUCK IN THE MECHANISM!

GLAZED DOUGHNUTS ARE THE ONE THING THAT THE DE-FORESTER 9000 CAN'T SHRED. IT'S A CURIOUS QUIRK OF PHYSICS.

RIGHT! LET'S GET ON WITH IT TH...

AW, SPOILSPORTS, THEY'VE GONE.

EVERYBODY, MEET THE NEWEST MEMBER OF OUR TEAM... **MONKEY!**

WHAT?

SHRIEK!

BUT...BUT... REMEMBER THE TIME HE GLUED MY **HANDS** TO MY **FACE!**

HEH HEH!

AND WHEN HE SAID HE WAS MY REAL FATHER.

PIG, THAT WASN'T FUNNY, I'M SORRY.

'S OKAY, DAD.

WELL, HE'S ONE OF US NOW, AND TOGETHER WE CAN COME UP WITH A PLAN TO **DEFEAT SKUNKY!**

YEAH!

WHOO!

PFFT. WHATEVER.

SINCE YOU RAN AWAY, I'M BRINGING THE DE-FORESTER TO **YOU!**

BWOO HAR HAR!

CRASH! SMASH!

THAT'S A WEIRD TREE.

THWACK!

ARGHFLE!

THAT WAS **MONKEY'S** IDEA!

THWACK!

YES. -:- COUGH -:-

I KINDA GUESSED THAT.

JAMIE

NEXT TIME: "THE MESSENGER!"

SOMETIMES MY FRIENDS REALLY ANNOY ME.

JUNE

"THE TRUTH-OMETER!"

SOMETIMES I GET FRUSTRATED WHEN PIG EATS ALL MY FOOD.

SOMETIMES I THINK I'M A **CHICKEN**.

GASP! THIS **TRUTHOMETER** REALLY WORKS! JUST BY WEARING THE SILVER HELMETS, WE'VE ALL UNWILLINGLY TOLD THE TRUTH!

TRUTH OMETER

WHAT A STRANGE, MYSTERIOUS GIFT TO SUDDENLY TURN UP.

BUK-BUK-BUKAWKK!

A PRESENT FOR ALL THE WOODLAND ANIMALS --FROM-- A friend!

MEANWHILE, AT THE LEAGUE OF DOOM SECRET H.Q...

HAR HAR HAR! MY PLAN IS GOING PERFECTLY!

IF I CAN'T SCARE THEM OUT OF THE WOODS, I'LL TRICK THEM INTO BEING BRUTALLY HONEST WITH EACH OTHER...

...SO THEY ALL FALL OUT AND WANT TO LEAVE THE WOODS BY THEMSELVES!

BZZT! HERE'S THE **BATTERY** FOR THE TRUTHOMETER, SIR! WHERE DO YOU WANT IT?

GASP!

YOU MEAN...THE TRUTHOMETER DOESN'T HAVE A BATTERY IN IT?!

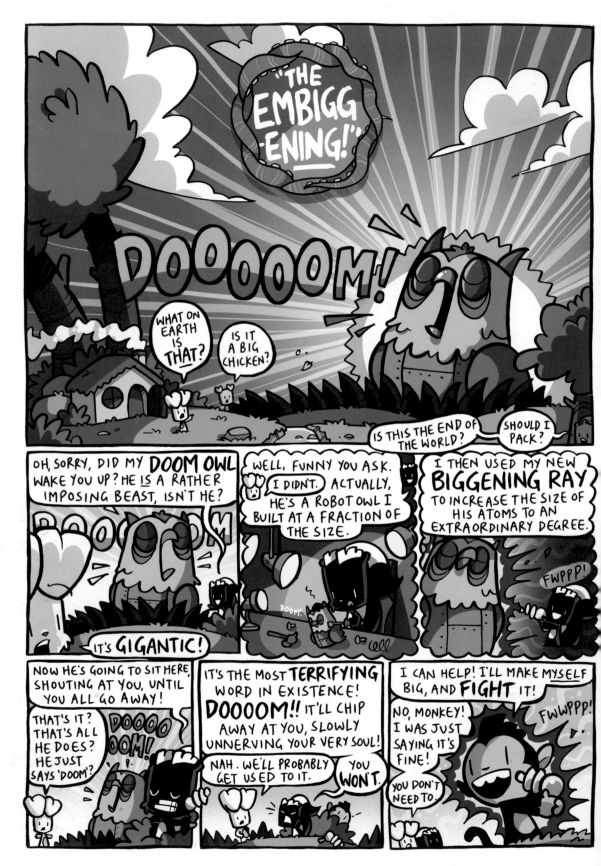

NURSE MONKEY!!

THE MOST **TERRIFYING, DERANGED** MEDICAL PROFESSIONAL EVER TO BE LET LOOSE ON A BUNNY WITH A SORE HEAD!

Nurse Kwalificay-shuns ~~~ Monkey ~~~ is a nurss!

HERE! IT'S TIME FOR YOUR...

DON'T BE SO... GLUG!

...MEDICINE!

WHAT- GLUG.. **IS** IT?

IN SKUNKY'S LAIR... HEY, WHERE DID MY BOTTLE OF **FART POTION** GO?

FRRPP!

OOH, EXCUSE ME!

A **WHISK**? WHAT'S THAT FOR?

IT'S FOR **LATER**. WHEN WE DO THE **SURGERY**.

HARHARHARR!

THE...WHAT?

FOR NOW, I THINK **THIS** PATIENT COULD DO WITH SOME FRESH AIR!

WHAT? NO! PUT ME DOWN!

WHEEL!

...AND A **HEDGE**!

OOMF!

SHOVE!

WE'RE BACK!

OH THANK GOODNESS, A **NURSE**!

WE GOT STUNG BY A **BEE**!

HMM, YOU'RE IN LUCK.

I BROUGHT MY WHISK! ARR HAR HAR HARRRR!

SCREEAM!

RUN! BOTH OF YOU, RUN!

WHIZZZZZ!

HOW LONG DO WE HAVE TO STAY IN THIS TREE, BUNNY?

UNTIL MONKEY CALMS DOWN.

RAH RAH!

SO MAYBE FOREVER.

FFRPP!

SORRY.

RAH RAH!

THE END... FOR NOW!

BUNNY vs MONKEY BOOK 6 OUT SOON!